Going to Church

**Sheila Hollins, John Swinton
and Katie Carpenter
illustrated by Lucy Bergonzi**

Beyond Words

London

36

First published in the UK 2017 by Books Beyond Words.

Text & illustrations © Books Beyond Words, 2017.

No part of this book may be reproduced in any form, or by any means, without the prior permission in writing from the publisher.

ISBN 978-1-78458-090-2

British Library Cataloguing-in-Publication Data

A catalogue record for this book is available from the British Library.

Printed by DX Imaging, Watford.

Books Beyond Words is a Community Interest Company registered in England and Wales (7557861).

Further information about the Books Beyond Words series can be obtained from Beyond Words' website: www.booksbeyondwords.co.uk.

Contents

Storyline

The following words are provided for readers and supporters who want some ideas about one possible story. Most readers make their own story up from the pictures.

1. It's Sunday. Mary and John watch 'Songs of Praise' while Anne and Alan wash the dishes.

2. Now Alan joins in. What fun!

3. Alan looks at his photo album.

4. He looks at photos of himself when he was younger. That's a nativity one. That one's at church.

5. Alan gets his cross out of the drawer. He has happy memories.

6. Alan waves goodbye. He is going out.

7. He stands outside a church. He thinks about going in.

8. Alan goes into the church.

9. Alan watches two ladies light candles.

10. Susie and Alan are both praying.

11. It's Sunday. Alan goes to church – he is not sure whether to go in. Lots of people are there.

12. A nice woman gives him a hymn book.

13. Alan finds a seat.

14. He loves singing! Other people look at him – is he too loud?

15. Oops. Alan is embarrassed.

16. The old man goes to communion. Alan doesn't know what to do.

17. Alan's had enough and is going home. He's a bit upset.

18. Alan doesn't eat his dinner. He is worried about something.

19. He tells John about the church.

20. John phones the vicar to introduce Alan.

21. They go to the church together to meet the vicar.

22. The vicar introduces Susie. He says Susie will look out for him.

23. Susie sits with Alan and shows him what to do.

24. Alan goes to communion. Susie helps him.

25. He's going to church again.

26. Alan is in church praying.

27. After the prayers, they all gather round for a chat, cup of tea and a biscuit.

28. Alan goes for a walk. He is day dreaming.

29. Oh dear, he didn't see the dog coming! That's a nasty fall!

30. Alan broke his leg. He has to stay at home.

31. Susie and Jane from church come to visit. Susie brings a present – it's a pot plant.

32. Alan enjoys having visitors. They have tea and biscuits together.

33. All of them are praying. Praying for Alan to get better soon.

34. The vicar comes to see if Alan is all right. They shake hands and are happy to see one another.

35. The vicar is glad to see Alan sing along with the TV. They have a good laugh together.

36. Alan is back in church. Everyone welcomes him back.

37. Singing! Alan knows the words – he doesn't need the book.

38. Alan is at home. He is smiling to himself and thinking. He wears his cross a lot of the time now.

Going to Church – an introduction

Many of us take for granted our ability to communicate and understand our world, but for some the barriers to communication are immense. Some people cannot read very well, or at all, and for them receiving and exploring information is a daily challenge. Without access to information to help make sense of life, people can feel overlooked and isolated, thus putting their wellbeing, health and happiness at risk. Belonging to a community reduces isolation, gives people meaning and purpose, and helps them contribute more fully.

Going to Church can support people to explore aspects of a church community, and to decide if they want to be part of it. It may help to address the spiritual questions and 'bigger' questions that all people have. Exploring the story may give someone the knowledge and confidence to join in, to meet new people and to generally have a higher quality of life.

This book is also a resource to help a church community actively consider how to reduce the barriers to participation that some members of society face, especially when there are communication difficulties. The pictures create a shared language between those reading the book together, making a more equal relationship. When read together by church members, with and without learning disabilities, the story will deepen understanding of people's experiences, the issues that they can encounter in church, and some of the ways in which we can work together to create stronger communities.

Guidance for families

Perhaps your adult son or daughter is living at home with you, or perhaps they have moved away to live on their own or in a shared house with others. It may be that they have had a rich church life throughout their childhood, known and loved by the local community. Depending on the church your family belongs to, they may have made their first communion, been confirmed, played a role as an altar server or been part of a ministry of welcome. Perhaps other family members have lapsed from attending church or your child has withdrawn from regular attendance.

In this story we see the main character Alan showing a renewed interest in going to church. But it's a new church and he finds it hard to get to know the new community and church leader on his own.

If going to church has always been part of your son or daughter's life, it is important that you explain this to the people who will be supporting them if they move to a new home.

46

Guidance for supporters

Sometimes support workers may be unfamiliar with what happens at church and why people go to church, or perhaps they belong to a different faith. They may lack confidence in supporting someone to make the first steps in going to a new church, or in regularly attending a church that they already know.

It is important for support workers to recognise how their own lack of confidence, or even feelings of ambivalence towards someone else's beliefs, are likely to affect the person's own wishes.

For many people, going to church is an essential part of their weekly calendar and participating in the life of the church is vital for them. If support issues make it hard for them to attend church and be part of the community, it can have an enormous impact on their quality of life.

Sometimes a person will have grown up in a church-going family but their current home is in a new place where they are not known in the local church community. Perhaps the care provider doesn't know about the person's faith background. Participating in the familiar shared rituals of prayer and worship can be healing and reassuring for someone who is still getting used to a new life in a new place.

Remember that everyone is made up of lots of different identities. They may be a person with a learning disability; they will also be a son or daughter, even if their parents have died; they may also be, for example, a person of colour, a friend, a sibling, a shop assistant and so forth. If they are also a person with a religious faith, it is just as important that they have the opportunity to explore and express this identity too.

To understand a person's faith and support them to be part of a faith community, it will help to take cues from their behaviour and interests. In this story Alan begins to show his interest in going to church by watching a religious programme on TV, looking at photos and belongings from his past, and finally by visiting a new church.

Be open to looking at old photos and artefacts with the person you support. This may open up new conversations and give hints about things that have been important to them in the past or aspects of their spiritual life that may not be being addressed in their current situation. Make sure that faith forms part of conversations that you have with the person's family, too, if they are involved. This will help you take account of the person's culture and background, and ensure that these identities are not lost.

Guidance for church communities

An inclusive Church

Going to Church aims to help church communities to offer a ministry of hospitality alongside people with learning disabilities. It is also intended to help support workers to understand how to support people to participate fully in their church community.

The thinking behind the book draws some of its inspiration from disability theology. The word 'theology' simply means the things that we know about God. Disability theology asks how what we know about God affects the ways in which we understand and respond to the experience of disability. The question for disability theology is: 'What might it mean for a person to be profoundly disabled, fully human and indeed quite beautiful just as they are?' Churches should be places where that question is answered with love, hospitality and genuine acceptance.

Churches are places that celebrate human diversity and difference, and where we share an understanding that God accepts all of us just as we are. When we recognise that, we can begin to build communities where difference is simply accepted.

Barriers to inclusion

It is surprising to discover that many barriers to inclusion are things we don't notice, rather than the more obvious barrier of transport or an inaccessible building. One of the things that the writers of this book have noticed in our conversations with congregations across the country is that churches often say things like, "We don't have any people with learning disabilities here, so we don't really need to make any adjustments." If there are no people with learning disabilities in our congregations perhaps we should wonder why that is and see if that wondering can bring about positive changes. Some attitudinal barriers to inclusion are:

1. Misunderstandings about what disability actually is. Some people assume that the experience of having a learning disability is a problem. If we think of learning disability as a problem to be solved then we will look upon people with learning disabilities in that same way. People with learning disabilities are not problems; they are, like all of us, people to be loved.

2. Thinking that being with people with learning disabilities is a specialised ministry. It is not unusual for churches to have disability ministry, which assumes being with people with disabilities is something that is the responsibility of a small dedicated group. When this happens, people with learning disabilities find themselves separated from the rest of the congregation, and the congregation is excluded from receiving the gifts that people with learning disabilities will bring.

3. Thinking that being with people with disabilities is an aspect of pastoral care. People with learning disabilities do not need special care, they need to be accepted in the same way that everyone

else is accepted. Including people with learning disabilities is best framed in terms of discipleship rather than pastoral care.

Practical tips for welcoming people with learning disabilities

Churches do not need to have a special ministry to welcome people with learning disabilities. 1 Corinthians 3:16–17 says: "Don't you realize that all of you together are the temple of God and that the Spirit of God lives in you?" The key to a genuinely inclusive community of belonging is to learn to recognise all people as valued, and to know that if one person is excluded we should all experience sadness.

Being alongside people with learning disabilities is not a ministry just for those people who are interested in such things. It is for all of us, together. There is nothing special that churches need to do, other than to make sure that everyone is cared for and accepted just as they are; that's how we become a community. It is true that some of us will need more help than others in certain areas, but all of us have gifts that which benefit everyone. In order to welcome people we need to love one another in our differences. Love means making sure that in our words and in our actions, we always say to one another, "It's good that you exist; it's good that you are in this world!"*

At a basic level this means that we need to be patient with one another, to allow all of our actions to be guided by kindness and not just a desire

*Josef Pieper, *Faith, Hope, Love* (San Francisco, Ca.: Ignatius, 1997)

to solve problems or 'get things done'. People with learning disabilities have a huge amount to offer to our congregations. The Church's task is to help that contribution to flourish. This will mean creatively looking for opportunities where people with disabilities can find the best way to contribute, and looking for ways in which we can get to know the person as a person. Invite people with learning disabilities, their supporters and their families to come and take part in the church. Some practical suggestions might be:

- Develop a sermon series based around passages, such as the one above, looking at the issues, not simply of including people with learning disabilities, but also in terms of what it actually means to be an inclusive community of belonging where everyone has a place.

- Explore ways of actively inviting people with learning disabilities, their carers and supporters to various events within your church community.

- Consider looking at the ways in which your church is disability-friendly and disability-unfriendly. Try to involve the whole congregation in a way that gives ownership of the initiative to everyone.

- Reflect on the question: what does it mean for this person with a learning disability to be a disciple with a vocation, a calling from God, to do something within this congregation? What is the gift that this person brings? How best can we receive it?

- Consider signing up to the Living Fully Charter (see page 53).

The Living Fully Charter: Living Fully within the Church

Because we are created in the image of God, we will:

- Show unconditional love; do as Jesus did, valuing all people of all abilities.

- Each be the glue that joins people together to celebrate themselves and their creation, no matter their body form and way of communicating.

- Show that each of us is loved by God, and that we are each and everywhere in the presence of God. We will be a witness for Christ and follow him.

- Celebrate being a Eucharistic people by enabling all to truly live out his/her vocation.

- Be creative artists in the work of God and in response to God's call, helping all to see and treat one another as unique individuals, each as God's work of art, rather than by labels that limit and exclude.

- Ensure that people of all abilities and disabilities feel invited, welcomed, and received as full members of God's community.

- Commit to helping others find and experience their own innate sense of worth and belonging, because we bear the image of God, we are the Body of Christ and we are inspired by Holy Scripture and the life of Jesus.

Because we are called to love all people, we will:

- Love God, love others, treat and serve everyone the same.

- Lead by example, seek positive change and foster a culture of justice and belonging.

- Help people to find peace and feel welcome in the Church.

- Reach out by invitation and welcoming people from all over the world, especially people who have been disabled and excluded.

- Attend to, receive, listen and make time for persons with disabilities and their families to express their faith, needs, gifts, and call to discipleship.

- Be evangelisers of all abilities: to EveryBody and with EveryBody.

- Together, develop creative skills in communication and access. Our faith communities will be accessible to all and a place of belonging for all.

We believe that the Church where persons with disabilities are present is:

- A place where creative ministry and friendship are an ordinary way of being together.

- A place where we 'Live Fully' within a culture of belonging.

- A community of love, joy, welcome and an invitation to reflect the image of God in the world.

- A space to share in faith and grow in friendship.

- A community where all people can respond to their call to be a disciple of Christ and enjoy ministering and evangelising with others.

- A community where each person can live out their innate uniqueness and rightful place in the world and community of faith.

- A community that sees beyond the labels and sees the person, not the disability or impairment.

- A witness to love at the heart of the Church.

- A community 'Living Fully' and giving witness to love in worship and service.

The Charter was created at the Living Fully events in Rome, June 2016, co-organised by the Pontifical Council for Culture and The Kairos Forum (see page 56). It is intended as a cross-denominational resource. The term 'EveryBody' was developed by the research project "EveryBody has a Story: Meeting people with intellectual disability and responding to their spiritual and religious needs", by The Kairos Forum.

Useful resources

Resources and organisations in the UK

Disability Matters
A free e-learning resource developed by the Royal College of Paediatrics and Child Health. Disability Matters aims to change fears, ideas and attitudes towards disability. It includes materials relevant for church leaders and volunteers. Beyond Words provided some materials for the programme.
www.disabilitymatters.org.uk

Church of England
The Church of England has produced guidance on welcoming people with learning disabilities, which can be downloaded from its website.
Opening the Doors: Ministry with people with learning disabilities and people on the autistic spectrum.
www.churchofengland.org/media/39672/gs1725.pdf

Several Anglican dioceses also have helpful information on their websites.
Welcome, Inclusion, Respect, Diocese of West Yorkshire and the Dales
www.westyorkshiredales.anglican.org/content/disability-and-inclusion
Welcome, Inclusion, Respect, Diocese of Oxford
www.oxford.anglican.org/mission-ministry/faith-in-action/disability

The Kairos Forum for People with Intellectual or Cognitive Disorders
The Kairos Forum aims to highlight and respond to the spiritual and religious needs of people

56

with disabilities in order to create 'Communities of Belonging', within both religious and secular settings. It provides specialist services and resources to enable and empower people with disabilities to experience dignity, respect, care, access and authentic participation within communities.
en-gb.facebook.com/The-Kairos-Forum-256066607804602/

Foundation for People with Learning Disabilities (**FPLD**)

FPLD offers free resources for staff, support workers, churches and people with learning disabilities on religion and spirituality. The following leaflets and documents are all free to download on the website.

Why Are We Here? Accessible summary

What is Important to You? A booklet for people with learning disabilities

No Box to Tick, A booklet for carers of people with learning disabilities

Spirituality and the Lives of People with Learning Disabilities

Religious expression: a fundamental human right

What about Faith?

www.mentalhealth.org.uk/learning-disabilities/publications

Prospects

Prospects, now part of Livability, is a Christian support provider, which provides information and resources for people with learning disabilities and for churches to support them. The website also has a listing of disability-friendly churches, with trained leaders and welcome teams.
www.prospects.org.uk

L'Arche

Today there are 147 communities of L'Arche in 35 countries on five continents. In L'Arche communities people living with learning disabilities, and those who come to help them, share daily life together with mutual respect. For more than 50 years, the experience of L'Arche is that this shared life opens new paths of friendship and spiritual growth in communities that are open to people of all denominations and faiths.
www.larche.org.uk

Churches for All

A partnership of UK Christian disability organisatiions aimng to help churches create and sustain an environment where disabled people can participate fully in church life for the benefit of all.
www.churches for all.org.uk

Inclusive Church

A membership organisation for churches and individuals uniting together for an inclusive church, advocating a non-discriminatory approach across a number of social issues. In partnership with the Church of St Martin in the Fields, they organise an annual Disability Conference.
https://inclusive-church.org.uk /disability

Centre for Spirituality, Health and Disability

A research and resource centre focused on providing new practical and theoretical resources designed to improve the spiritual lives of people with disabilities. The following articles are free to download.
Whose Story Am I? Redescribing Profound Intellectual Disability in the Kingdom of God
Building a church for strangers
www.abdn.ac.uk/cshad

Disability, Religion and Spirituality Resources
A comprehensive listing of articles, books and media.
http://kc.vanderbilt.edu/kennedy_pdfs/spirituality/
disabilityreligionspiritualityresources1108.pdf

Making SMSCD Special: Sensory engagement with scripture
A film made by Culham St Gabriel's Trust in collaboration with Swiss Cottage Teaching School Alliance. It explains how a multi-sensory approach can enable children and young people with complex needs to engage with scripture.
http://thesendhub.co.uk/sensory-engagement-with-scripture/

Books and written resources

Gleanings
A free newsletter from the American Association on Intellectual and Developmental Disabilities, Religion and Spirituality Division. It compiles blogs, videos, books, articles, and conferences on disability issues, edited by Rev Bill Gaventa.
https://aaiddreligion.org/newsletters/

Mental Health: The inclusive church resource, Jean Vanier, John Swinton (Darton, Longman &Todd, 2014)
This book aims to educate, to reflect and to provide advice and guidance about church inclusivity. It contains personal experiences, a resource section, and practical advice.

Disability in the Christian Tradition: A reader, Brian Brock and John Swinton (Eerdmans, 2012)
This book brings together the views of Christian leaders throughout history. Experts in theology

and disability studies offer clear commentary and highlight important themes.

Enabling Church: A Bible-based resource towards the full inclusion of disabled people, Gordon Temple with Lin Ball (SPCK, 2012)
This resource for church leaders, congregations and small groups looks at what the Bible says about disability – and what the Church could do in response.

Making Church Accessible to All: Including disabled people in church life, Tony Phelps-Jones (The Bible Reading Fellowship, 2013)
This book looks at the obstacles that church can put in the way and the practicalities of establishing an effective ministry.

You and Your Child: Making sense of learning disabilities, Sheila Hollins and Martin Hollins (Karnac Books, 2005)
This book describes the experiences of five families in bringing up a child who is different, drawing extensively on the parents' voices.

'The Challenges Faced by People with Intellectual Disabilities and their Families', Hollins S., Lodge K-M. *INTAMS review* 21 (2015).
The authors explore the challenges and joys of parenting a child, including an adult child, with a learning disability through a Christian lens.

Related titles in the Books Beyond Words series

Speaking Up for Myself (2002) by Sheila Hollins, Jackie Downer, Linette Farquarson and Oyepeju Raji, illustrated by Lisa Kopper. Having a learning disability and being from an ethnic minority group can make it hard to get good services. Natalie learns to fix problems by being assertive and getting help from someone she trusts.

Michelle Finds a Voice (2016, 2nd edition) by Sheila Hollins and Sarah Barnett, illustrated by Denise Redmond. Michelle cannot speak and is unable to communicate her thoughts and feelings. She feels isolated and unhappy. Michelle and her carers try signing, symbols and electronic aids to find a solution that works.

When Mum Died and *When Dad Died* (2014, 4th edition) by Sheila Hollins and Lester Sireling, illustrated by Beth Webb. These books take a gentle, honest and straightforward approach to death and grief in the family. The pictures tell the story of the death of a parent in a simple but moving way. The approach is non-denominational.

George Gets Smart (2001) by Sheila Hollins, Margaret Flynn and Philippa Russell, illustrated by Catherine Brighton. George's life changes when he learns how to keep clean and smart. People no longer avoid being with him and he enjoys the company of his work mates and friends.

Authors and artist

Sheila Hollins is the Founding Editor of Books Beyond Words and Emeritus Professor of Psychiatry of Disability at St George's University of London. She was a consultant psychiatrist working with people with learning disabilities for over 30 years. She is Honorary Professor in the Department of Religion and Theology at the University of Durham and a member of the Pontifical Commission for the protection of children and vulnerable adults.

John Swinton is Professor in Practical Theology and Pastoral Care in the School of Divinity, Religious Studies and Philosophy at the University of Aberdeen. He has a background in mental health and learning disability nursing and healthcare chaplaincy and writes about practical theology, mental health, spirituality and human wellbeing and the theology of disability. He is the Director of Aberdeen University's Centre for Spirituality, Health and Disability.

Katie Carpenter organises a Beyond Words Book Club which meets monthly. She is currently helping to establish and lead a Book Club at the Chadsgrove Learning Centre, for students 19–25 years, in Bromsgrove. Her hobbies are drama and cookery.

Lucy Bergonzi has worked as a muralist, theatre designer and community artist. For many years she worked in the voluntary and community sector, with wide experience of supporting people with learning disabilities. She co-authored and illustrated *A Day at the Beach* with Kent Book Clubs for Books Beyond Words. Lucy's website is www.lucybergonzi.co.uk.

Acknowledgments

We thank our editorial advisors David Barnett, Nigel Hollins and Sarah Hammond for their ideas and advice about what was needed in the pictures.

We are grateful for the advice and support of our advisory group, which included Cristina Gangemi (Kairos Forum, Disability Advisor to Catholic Church), Sue Day (Development head for Caritas and St Joseph's Pastoral centre), Hazel Morgan (formerly Foundation for People with Learning Disabilities), Christine Burke (Foundation for People with Learning Disabilities), Rev Tim Goode (Disability Advisor to Southwark Diocese), Lorna Humphries (trainee psychiatrist), Barry Carpenter (Katie's supporter), Nicky Sharples (Nigel's supporter).

Many thanks to all individuals and groups who trialled the pictures: Queens Road Baptist Church, Broadstairs; Epsom Book Group; Plymouth Highbury Trust – part of Plymouth People First; Michael Batt Foundation; Ashford Book Group; Edenbridge Book Club – Library Ladies; Katie Carpenter's Book Club (Kirsty, Helen, Richard, Sue, Nicholas, Jess, Nicola); Ridleys, Plymouth Guild – part of Plymouth People First; Yarway Art Studio – linked to Plymouth People First; Cliftonville Library LD Book Club, Dover, Kent (David Tate, Darren O'Sullivan, Alex Knight, Neil Kerby, Samantha Byrne, supporter: Hannah Saunders); Folkestone Book Club; People First Dorset (James Carter, Diane Childs, Nesta Oram, William Parmiter, Dick Corbett-Winder, Lisa Dixon, Laura Kerr, supporter: Hazel Morgan); Bookworms,

Tunbridge Wells; Word in the Hand Book Club in Canterbury Library; Dover Discovery Book Club; Arrcc Ltd Folkestone; Pluss – part of Plymouth People First; The Grange, Bookham; St Joseph's Book Club – Caritas; "Neat Ideas" Group in Aberdeen (Elm Class at Woodlands School, Aberdeen, supporters: Karen Gebbie-Smith, Stephanie Brock); Woodlands School, Aberdeen.

Our illustrator Lucy is grateful to her models Adam, Alice, Becci, Daniel, Gemma, James, Jo, Jon, Lilli, Ruby and Steve for their help when she was creating the pictures for *Going to Church*.

Finally we are grateful to Caritas Westminster, Mrs L D Rope Third Charitable Settlement and Westhill Endowment Trust for their generous financial support of this book.

Beyond Words: publications and training

Books Beyond Words are stories for anyone who finds pictures easier than words. A list of all Beyond Words publications, including print and eBook versions of Books Beyond Words titles, and where to buy them, can be found on our website:

www.booksbeyondwords.co.uk

Workshops for family carers, support workers and professionals about using Books Beyond Words are provided regularly in London, or can be arranged on request in other localities or to cover specific areas of interest. Self-advocates are welcome. For information about forthcoming workshops see our website or contact us:

email: admin@booksbeyondwords.co.uk

Video clips showing our books being read are also on our website and YouTube channel: www.youtube.com/user/booksbeyondwords and on our DVD, *How to Use Books Beyond Words*.

How to read this book

This is a story for people who find pictures easier to understand than words. It is not necessary to be able to read any words at all.

1. Some people are not used to reading books. Start at the beginning and read the story in each picture. Encourage the reader to hold the book themselves and to turn the pages at their own pace.

2. Whether you are reading the book with one person or with a group, encourage them to tell the story in their own words. You will discover what each person thinks is happening, what they already know, and how they feel. You may think something different is happening in the pictures yourself, but that doesn't matter. Wait to see if their ideas change as the story develops. Don't challenge the reader(s) or suggest their ideas are wrong.

3. Some pictures may be more difficult to understand. It can help to prompt the people you are supporting, for example:

- I wonder who that is?
- I wonder what is happening?
- What is he or she doing now?
- I wonder how he or she is feeling?
- Do you feel like that? Has it happened to you/ your friend/ your family?

4. You don't have to read the whole book in one sitting. Allow people enough time to follow the pictures at their own pace.

5. Some people will not be able to follow the story, but they may be able to understand some of the pictures. Stay a little longer with the pictures that interest them.